HORIZONS

Learning to Read

Level B
Workbook 1

Siegfried Engelmann

Owen Engelmann

Karen Lou Seitz Davis

SRA

A Division of The McGraw-Hill Companies

Columbus, Ohio

Illustration Credits

Shirley Beckes, Daniel Clifford, Doug Cushman, Susanne DeMarco, Len Ebert, John Edwards and Associates, Kersti Frigell, Ethel Gold, Meryl Henderson, Susan Jerde, Louis Pappas, Jim Shough

SRA/McGraw-Hill

A Division of The McGraw·Hill Companies

Send all inquiries to:
Glencoe/McGraw-Hill
8787 Orion Place
Columbus, OH 43240

ISBN 0-02-830787-9

11 12 13 14 15 POH 09 08 07 06

 •   • Be home by nine.

 •   • I won't be late.

 •   • Row, row, row . . .

card	store	wheel	sunburn

plane

stick

1. Who asked Bob to sing with her? _____

2. Bob's dad told him to be home by _____.
   • five   • one   • nine

3. Who got to sing first? _____
   • Sid   • Jan   • Bob

4. Did Jan sing just one time? _____

5. Do you think Bob will be home on time? _____

barn   train   dream

lean   her   first   boat

Side 2

late   on   not   home   time   nine   by

I hope I am _____
_____ .

sky	shirt	hat	king

		cup

bug

1. Who got to sing first? _____

   • Jan's mom   • Jan   • Bob

2. Who told Jan that Bob needs a turn?

   _____

      • Jan's mom   • Bob's dad   • Bob

3. Who was singing, "You are my sunshine"?

   _____

         • Jan's mom   • Jan   • Bob

4. Did Bob sing just one time or lots of times?

   _____

5. Did Bob get home on time? _____

6. When will Bob sing with Jan next?

   _____

      • now   • not for a while   • in a while

lead	over	eat	playing
away	start	chop	butter

3

bitter   fox   tub   better

This butter is
_____
_____
_____.

_____
- - - - - - - - -
_____

tr<u>ai</u>l   five   robber   baby   winter

- - - - - ring

_____

1. When did the fox sell bitter butter?

_ _ _ _ _ _ _ _ _ _ _ _ _

_____

   • this year   • last year

2. When did the fox make sweet butter?

_ _ _ _ _ _ _ _ _ _ _ _

_____

                                    _____

                                    _ _ _ _ _ _ _ _ _ _ _ _ _

3. The fox sold bitter butter to _____.
   • the little turtle   • the fox   • Bob

4. What did the turtles make with the butter?

_ _ _ _ _ _ _ _ _ _ _ _ _

_____

      • a car   • a cake   • a meal

                                    _____

                                    _ _ _ _ _ _

5. This year, the fox had butter in a _____.
        • car   • pan   • tub

| car | then | day | sister |
| boat | train | birds | when |

rat   sweet   fox   bitter   butter

It's _____
_____.

It's too _____
_____.

Sweet,
sweet
_____
_____
_____

_____

_____

boat   swim   run   e at

_____ | _____ | _____ | _____

4

1. The fox filled _____

   with butter.
   - c<u>a</u>rts and vans   - tubs and p<u>ai</u>ls   - pots and pans

2. He l<u>oa</u>ded the pots and pans into his _____.
   - c<u>a</u>rt   - c<u>a</u>r   - van

3. Who did he meet first? _____
   - b<u>ir</u>ds   - a rat   - a turtle

4. Did the b<u>ir</u>ds taste his butter? _____

5. Did the rat taste his butter? _____

6. How much butter did the fox sell? _____
   - a lot   - some   - n<u>o</u>ne

Side 2Side 2

© SRA/McGraw-Hill. All rights reserved.© SRA/McGraw-Hill. All rights reserved.

fine   bitter   cake   b<u>ar</u>n

This _____

is _____ .

___

f<u>ar</u>m   pants   st<u>or</u>m   fishing

bed

bag

1. What did a goat make with bitter butter?

   _ _ _ _ _ _ _ _ _ _ _ _ _ _ _
   _____

   • cakes   • rolls   • crackers

   _____
   _ _ _ _ _ _
2. Did the goat like them? _____

3. The ducks, pigs, rams, and cows were
   _ _ _ _ _ _ _ _ _ _ _ _ _ _ _ _ _
   _____.

   • in the pond   • in the barn   • in the road

   _____
   _ _ _ _ _ _ _ _ _ _ _ _ _ _ _
4. They told the fox to _____.
   • make rolls   • eat cake   • go home

5. The fox said, "I will make a cake for the
   _____ "
   _ _ _ _ _ _ _ _ _ _ _ _ _ _ _
   _____.

   • pigs and goats   • summer Cake Bake
          • winter party

   _____
   _ _ _ _ _ _
6. The cake was _____.
   • bad   • fine   • bitter

dress	fox	cake	c<u>a</u>rt	hat	wig

A cow at e grass. •   •

A turtle dov e into a pond. •   •

A duck sat on a cow. •   •

1. What did the fox have on?

_____

- -

_____

- a hat, a dress, and a wig   • a hat, a shirt, and a sk<u>i</u>rt
- a wig, a c<u>oa</u>t, and a t<u>ai</u>l

2. _____ cakes were in the summer Cake Bak<u>e</u>.

- 50   • 10   • 20

3. Whi<u>ch</u> cake did the cake tasters like best?

- -

_____

- a brown cake   • a yellow cake   • a red cake

4. Wh<u>o</u> bak<u>e</u>d that cake? _____

5. Will the fox sell lots of sweet butter now? _____

6. Now the birds, <u>pigs, rats, cows,</u> and turtles think the

butter is _____.

- bad   • fine   • bitter

had   go   flying   sing   am

I _____ _____ _____ .

Go, Tom, _____
_____ .

wing   dream   tub   cow

dress   yellow

Side 1

1. Who had a fe<u>e</u>r of flying? _____

_____

2. Did <u>Tom's</u> <u>brothers</u> and sisters have a fe<u>e</u>r of flying?

_ _ _ _ _ _ _

_____

_____

3. When did his mother tell Tom it was time for him to fly?

_ _ _ _ _ _ _ _ _ _ _ _ _ _ _ _ _ _ _ _

_____

- just befor<u>e</u> winter   • just befor<u>e</u> spring
- just befor<u>e</u> summer

_____

4. She told him to jump on her back and _____.

- sleep   • hang on   • sit

_____

5. Did Tom fly? _____

_____

6. <u>Tom's</u> <u>brothers</u> and sisters went flying and had

_ _ _ _ _ _ _

_____.

- fun   • fe<u>e</u>r   • feet

8

birds   summer   rid e

It feels like

_____

_ _ _ _ _ _ _ _ _

_____.

I am going to see the

_____

_ _ _ _ _ _ _ _ _

_____.

She rocked the baby. •

Mother at e the chips. •

The fox licked the box. •

1. What was the winter like?

_____

- - - - - - - - - - - - - - - - - - -

_____

    • h<u>ar</u>d and hot   • h<u>ar</u>d and cold   • hotter and hotter

2. Irma said, "We have only seen _____.

      • a d<u>ar</u>k sky   • a d<u>ar</u>k sun   • hills

3. Who said, "I will ride my bike to the lake"? _____

      • Bob   • <u>Ir</u>ma   • V<u>er</u>n

4. What did <u>Ir</u>ma plan to see? _____

    • birds   • a hill of mud   • goats

5. Who wore a big hat? _____

6. What was the only thing V<u>er</u>n wore?

_____

- - - - - - - - - - - - - - - - - - -

_____

    • black pants   • a big hat   • sh<u>or</u>t pants

beach   sun   V<u>er</u>n   lak<u>e</u>

rocks   bik<u>e</u>   spring   happy   ship   sit   brother   winter

1. How did Vern and Irma get to the lake?

_ _ _ _ _ _ _ _ _ _ _ _ _ _

_____

   • in boats   • on bikes   • in a car

2. Which one was as white as snow?

_ _ _ _ _ _ _ _ _ _ _ _

_____

   • Bob   • Vern   • the little turtle

3. Which shore did Vern like?

_ _ _ _ _ _ _ _ _ _ _ _ _ _ _ _

_____

   • the shore with shade   • the sandy shore

_____

_ _ _ _ _ _ _ _ _ _ _ _

4. Who liked the shore with birds? _____

5. Why did Irma go to the far shore?

_ _ _ _ _ _ _ _ _ _ _ _ _ _ _

_____

   • to see birds   • to swim   • to sleep

6. Vern said, "I will have fun _____ "

_ _ _ _ _ _ _ _ _ _ _ _ _ _

_____.

   • on my bike   • in the shade   • in the sun

Side 2

1. _____   2. _____

3. _____   4. _____

  Tom was a bird. It was spring, but Tom was not set to fly. He had a f<u>ea</u>r of flying. He told his mother, "I can do lots of things, but I do not think I can fly."

---

or   ol

---

1. sink	1. tasted	1. getting
2. brothers	2. tir<u>e</u>d	2. dress
3. h<u>u</u>rry	3. roll	3. best
4. were	4. h<u>a</u>rd	4. yello<u>w</u>

Then just before summer started, Tom's mom told him, "It's time for you to fly. Jump up on my back and hang on." He did that. And his mom sailed into the sky.

Each day, Tom's brothers and sisters went flying, but Tom stayed at home. Each day, the others came home and told what fun they had. Tom did not have fun.

fold first

Then Tom's mother said, "It is more fun if you hold your wings up."

After he did that, was he still on his mom's back? No. He was not on his mom's back. He was flying. And it was fun.

The end.

fold

Can Tom Fly? 10

It was spring. The other birds were set to fly, but Tom was not set to fly.

Tom had a fear of flying. He told his mom, "I can run, and I can read. I can sit, and I can sing. But I do not think I can fly."

1. Who stayed at the sandy beach? _____

_____

2. Did Vern stay in the shade? _____

_____

3. At first, Vern turned _____.
   - very pink   • a little pink   • red

_____

4. When Vern got home, he was _____.

_____

5. Who asked him why he didn't take a hat and a shirt?
   _____

   _____

   • Bob   • his mother   • Al

_____

6. Vern said, "I didn't _____."
   • think   • stink   • pink

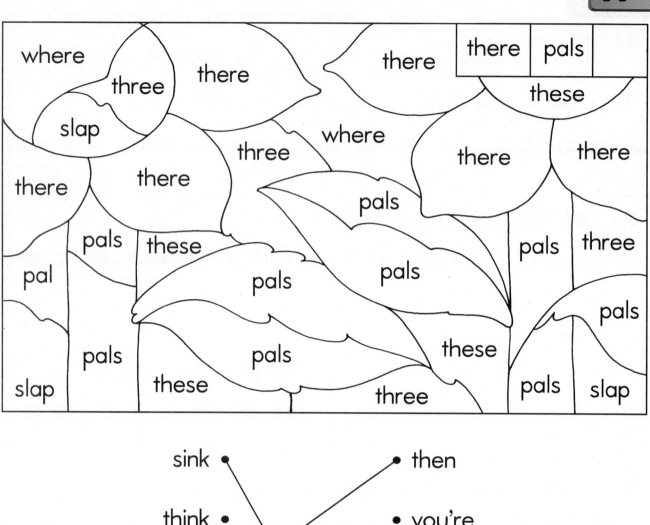

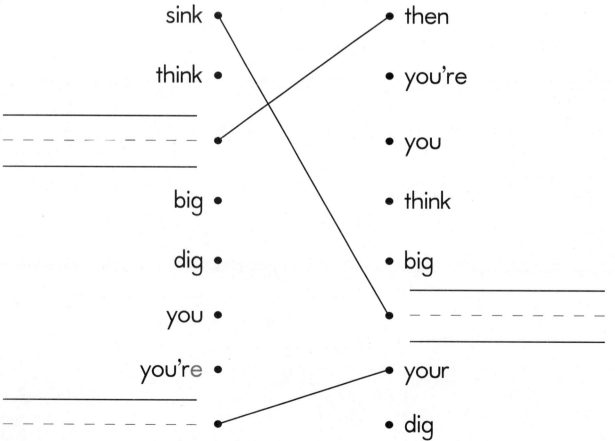

sink • • then

think • • you're

_____

- - - - - - - - - - •

_____

big • • think

dig • • big

you • •

you're • • your

_____

- - - - - - - - - - •

_____

pail   goat   fox   toad   pig

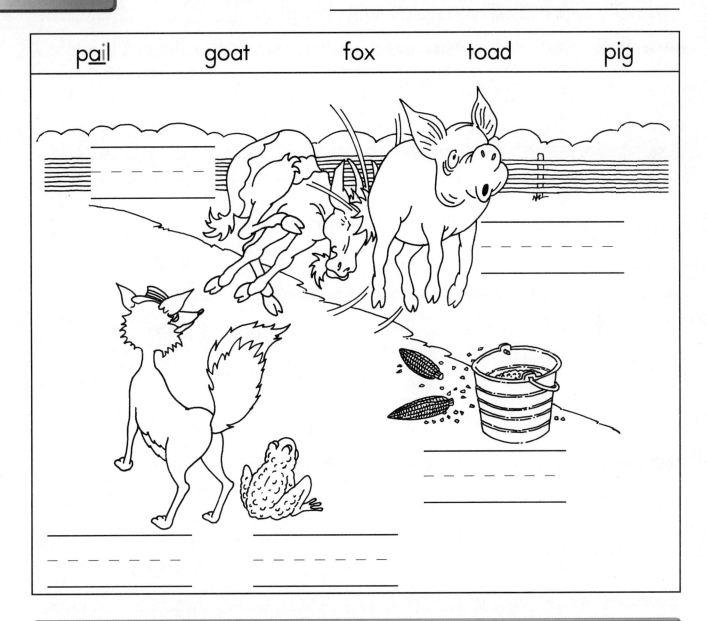

mom •
     • sand on a shore

pond •
     • mother

bitter •
     • a little lake

beach •
     • ants and bees

bugs •
     • It tastes bad.

1. Did Gorman like to play with his pals? _____

2. Did the pals like to play with Gorman? _____

3. What were his pals playing with? _____
    - a ram   - a p**ai**l   - a boat

4. Who said, "I m**ay** be the best p**ai**l jumper there is"?
    _____

    - the f**ar**mer   - Bob   - G**or**man

5. Who did Gorman run into? _____
    - the f**ar**mer   - the pig   - the cr**ow**

soap	pals	pails	there	~~pals~~	(there)
these	maps	pans	those	there	3	4

soap	pails	lips	where	three	the	pals
there	lips	naps	here	where		slap
then	pans	the	last	those	slap	then	pails
here	pal	pals	these		there

Side 2

B ____

S ____

- • Let's go in the cave.

- • We must get cl<u>ea</u>n.

- • I hate mud.

- • Mud is fun.

duck	pots	cows	shade

	dress	
cakes		

1. Who went for a hike? _____ and _____
   • Sid   • Bob   • Jan

2. After six miles, they came to _____.
   • a b<u>ar</u>n   • a pond   • a cave

3. Who said, "Mud is fun"? _____

4. Who said, "I hate mud"? _____

5. Was there mud in the cave? _____

6. Sid got _____ mud on his pants.
   • brown   • black   • red

not   s<u>ea</u>l   swimming   got   go   h<u>ar</u>d

This mud is _____ _____.

Let's _____

happy •   • many mil<u>e</u>s away

plan<u>e</u> •   • not sad

trees •   • You can fly in it.

f<u>ar</u> •   • They have l<u>ea</u>ves.

1. The mud on Bob's and Sid's pants was _____.

   • black   • red   • brown

2. How did Sid and Bob get down the hill?

   _____

   • They rolled.   • They ran.   • They slid.

3. Why didn't Bob stand up?

   _____

   • He was tired.   • His pants were hard.

   • He was sleeping.

4. Who rolled Sid and Bob into the sea?

   _____

   • Gorman   • Jan   • three seals

5. Who said, "Let's go swimming"? _____

   • Gorman   • Jan   • a seal

clam   fun   hang   otter   on

hug •   • not h<u>a</u>rd

<u>e</u>asy •   • to hold with your <u>ar</u>ms

liked •   • not cl<u>ea</u>n

d<u>ir</u>ty •   • not hat<u>e</u>d

1. Ann was a _____.

   _____

   • shark   • clam   • fish

2. Ann said, "Why can't I swim with _____?"

   _____ "

   • sharks   • fish   • otters

3. Otters like to eat _____.

   _____

   • sharks   • goats   • clams

4. Ann told an otter to hide from _____.

   _____

   • a clam   • Bob   • a shark

5. Who takes Ann swimming? _____

   _____

   • her mom   • an otter   • a shark

shell	summer	saw
		fish

16

_____

- - - - - - - - - - - - - - - -

_____

_____

- - - - - - - - - - - -

1. Who was Tom? _____

- an otter   • a shark   • his dad

_____

_____

- - - - -

2. Did Tom listen to his mom and dad? _____

_____

_____

- - - - - - - - - - - - - - - -

3. At first, he followed a clam that _____.

- was stinking   • was sinking   • was pink

_____

4. Then he followed s<u>ea</u>ls

_____

- -

_____.

- for ten weeks   • for a mile or more

- after he got sore

_____

5. What did Tom see when he was near a weed?

_____

- - - - - - - - - - - - -

_____

- a s<u>ea</u>l   • his mom   • a shark

shark •   • something that is b<u>ur</u>ning

bike •   • what you h<u>ea</u>r with

fan •   • something that blows <u>ai</u>r on you

fire •   • a big fish with lots of teeth

<u>ea</u>rs •   • It has two wheels.

sinking	think	bring	any	~~any~~	thing
an	am	any	many	4	3
think	thing	things	an	sting	any
thin	thing	think	many	funny	any
thing	an	this	many	bring	sink

h<u>ur</u>t	yell	chase	shore	swim	pants

Tom   got   mom   shark   Not

I've _____ you now.

Many fish swam in a pond. •   •

A shark chased his tail. •   •

A seal was on the beach. •   •

1. Which otter yelled from beneath?

_____

- - - - - - - - - - - - - - - - -

_____

      • Tom   • Tom's mom   • Tom's dad

2. Who bit the shark's tail? _____

3. Which otter did the shark chase? _____

4. Tom's mom stopped _____.

      • in a cave   • in front of a rock   • to eat

5. Was Tom shocked? _____

farm •   • jump

hive •   • not slow

easy •   • a home for cows, sheep, and goats

leap •   • a home for bees

fast •   • not h<u>ar</u>d

A bird is on my <u>ar</u>m. •

A cop met a mole. •

Which tr<u>ai</u>l do we take? •

1. Who saved Tom? _____

    • his mom   • a seal   • Bob

2. Where did Tom's mom stop? _____

    _____

    • in a cave   • in front of a rock

3. What did the shark run into? _____

    • Bob   • a rock   • a cave

4. Does that shark know that he is a shark? _____

5. What does the shark think he is? _____

    • a seal   • a meal   • Bob

6. Sam doesn't know that Tom is _____.

    • a fish   • a clam   • a meal

soak   you   help   save

We'll _____ _____.

_____, _____.

tractor	shell	swimming	street
		smile

| | | men |

1. Who did not listen well? _____

_____

2. Who kept telling her to listen better?

   _____

   - Tam's mom
   - Bob's dad
   - Jan's mom

3. One time, Tam and her mom went up _____.
   - a tree
   - a hill
   - the steps

4. Did Tam stay on the path? _____

5. One time, Tam's mom told Tam not to swim in

   _____.

   - the tub
   - the deep part
   - the pond

6. Who saved Tam? _____
   - a goat
   - Bob
   - two men

20

1. _____   2. _____

3. _____   4. _____

Bob and Sid went inside a cave. Sid said, "I feel my feet sinking in mud. Let's go." In a little while, they came from the cave. "We must get clean before that mud gets h<u>ar</u>d."

1. shark	1. very	1. saw
2. sn<u>ai</u>l	2. shell	2. doesn't
3. street	3. chased	3. many
4. swam	4. himself	4. because

Clams seem to have a big smile, but some clams are not happy. One sad clam was named Ann. Why was she sad? She did not like to stay in the sand with the other clams.

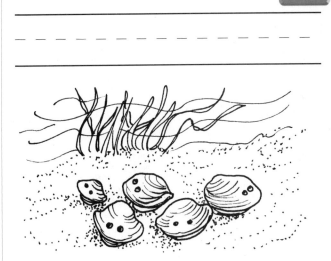

Ann said, "Why can't I swim with the otters?"

Her mom said, "That's silly. Otters eat clams. They don't swim with clams."

One day, a shark was swimming near the clams.

A little otter was swimming near the clams, too. The little otter did not see the shark. As the otter came close to Ann, she opened her shell and yelled, "Shark, shark. Hide, hide, hide."

The little otter hid in the weeds, and the shark went away. The next day, the otter came back. She said to the clam, "Thank you for saving me. What can I do in return?"

You know what Ann said, and you know what they did.

So if you ever see an otter swimming with a clam on its tail, you will know who they are.

The end.

fold first

fold

- "I will listen better."

- "Don't let anyone in."

- "You were very smart."

- "I am here to fix your TV."

- "I must tell the cops."

snail	trailer	summer	

pen

1. Where did Tam's mom go in this story?

- -

_____

• to the farm   • to the store   • to the barn

2. Before she left, Tam's mom told Tam not to let

- -

_____.

• anyone inside   • the cat in   • Jan sing

3. Did Tam do what her mom said? _____

4. A man told Tam that he came to fix the _____.

• car   • boat   • TV

5. The man was a _____.

• teacher   • cop   • robber

6. Who told the cops? _____

trailer   home   tractor   this   Bob

We are on the way
_____
_ _ _ _ _ _ _ _
_____.

I can run faster than
_____
_ _ _ _ _ _ _
_____.

☐ 1. Make a **T** over the tree.

☐ 2. Make an **O** under the tree.

☐ 3. Make a **T** on the fish.

1. How f<u>ar</u> from town was Jill's farm?

_____

- -

_____

   • ten miles   • three miles   • six miles

2. Where did she need to go? _____

   - - - - - - - - - - - -

   • to the farm   • to the store   • to see Bob

3. How did she get there? _____

   - - - - - - - - - - -

   • hik<u>e</u>d   • ran   • drove

4. Who was going to pick her up? _____

   - - - - - - - - - - - - -

   • Bob   • her mother   • her dad

5. What was her dad driv<u>ing</u>? _____

   - - - - - - - - - - - - - -

   • a car   • a tract<u>or</u>   • a tr<u>ai</u>ler

skunk  star   10

 star   9   skunk

star   blue

thank   dear   star   sunk

$\boxed{\text{st\underline{ar}} \\ 7}$

23

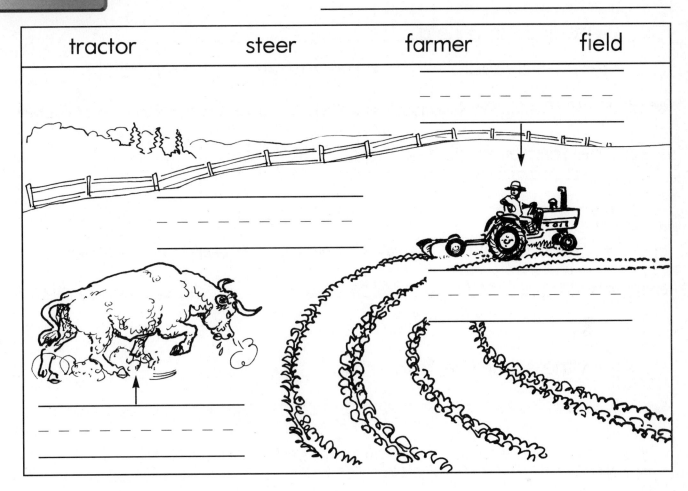

tractor steer farmer field

---

1. box
2. circle

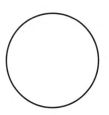 

☐ 1. Make an **e** in the circle.

☐ 2. Make a **b** on top of the circle.

☐ 3. Make a **T** over the box.

☐ 4. Make a **J** under the box.

1. Who lived in a field? _____

        • a steer   • the farmer   • Bob

2. The farmer said, "I will dig. Then I can _____,"

_____.

     • make a hole   • plant corn   • wake up a steer

3. Did the steer like farmers in his field? _____

4. Where does the steer plan to send the farmer?

_____

    • to a lake   • to his field   • to his home

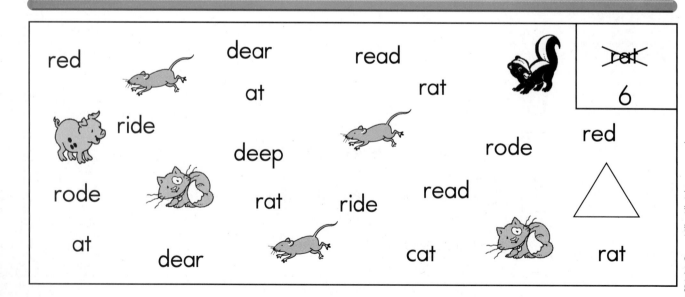

red   dear   read   ~~rat~~

at   rat   6

ride   deep   rode   red

rode   rat   ride   read

at   dear   cat   rat

24

1. circle
2. box

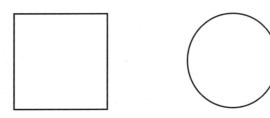

1. Make a **d** inside the box.

2. Make an **i** over the circle.

3. Make a **t** under the box.

4. Make a turtle over the box.

balls	beach	smile	otter	digging	bells

1. Where were the farmer and the steer?

      • in a field   • in a barn   • in Bob's home

2. Who ran into the tractor? _____

      • a steer   • a goat   • a farmer

3. Who went flying? _____

4. The steer landed on its _____.

      • feet   • seat   • back

5. The steer said, "I see _____.

      • stars   • barns   • bells

6. The steer said, "I hear _____.

dad   stones   Sandy   throw

I don't like to _____ _____.

little •   • what you hear with

grab •   • take

snow •   • small

ears •   • It's cold and white.

stones •   • small rocks

1. Sandy did not know how to _____.

   • roll   • swim   • throw

2. Did she try to throw b<u>a</u>lls and ston<u>e</u>s? _____

3. Who asked her to throw ston<u>e</u>s in the lake?

   _____

   • her mom   • her dad   • her brother

4. Who asked her to throw snow b<u>a</u>lls?

   _____

5. Sandy and her brother were in the _____.

   • back yard   • street   • front yard

6. What hit her in the back? _____

   • a hand   • a snow b<u>a</u>ll   • a snow man

Tom and the Shark

There once was an otter, and his name was Tom.
But Tom didn't listen to his dad or mom.

One day his mom told him, "Don't swim near the caves.
Because there's a shark who hunts in those waves."

But Tom started playing, and he wasn't really thinking.
He first chased a clam that seemed to be sinking.

Then he followed two seals that were close to the shore.
He followed those seals for a mile or more.

At last he stopped to see where he was.
He said, "I saw something swimming the way a shark does."

"Oh, oh," he said, as he hid near a weed.
"I hope this is not where sharks like to feed."

Tom's

But the shark came closer and showed many teeth.
And just at that moment, someone yelled from beneath.

"For a bigger meal, you can come after me."
The otter who spoke was Tom's mom, you see.

She swam and she dove and bit the shark's tail.
She told that shark, "You're as slow as a snail."

The shark chased Tom's mom as fast as a shot.
And said, "I've got you now." But Tom's mom said, "Not."

Just then Tom got a very bad shock.
His mom just stopped, in front of a rock.

As the shark came closer, did she stay where she was?
No, she darted to one side, the way an otter does.

The shark hit the rock with such a hard blow,
That he said to himself, "Who am I? I don't know."

Then he asked Tom's mom, "Can you tell me who I am?"
She said, "You're a very big seal, and your name is Sam."

So Tom has a pal who thinks he's a seal.
And Sam doesn't know that Tom is a meal.

The end.

Sandy   fire   the   Hiss

I must stop _____ _____.

1. Box the fish.
2. Make a **T** over the fish.
3. Circle the star.
4. Make a box under the bird.

1. What did Sandy see in the back yard?

_____

- a skunk   - a fire   - a tree

2. What made the fire start? _____

- a spark   - the sun   - a st<u>or</u>m

3. What was burning at first? _____

- leaves   - sticks   - rags

4. Why didn't Sandy's brother help her stop the fire?

_____

- He didn't see her.   - He didn't hear her.
- He was going for help.

5. What did Sandy throw at the fire? _____

- base<u>ba</u>lls   - snow flakes   - snow b<u>al</u>ls

6. Can Sandy throw things now? _____

1. Circle the fish.
2. Box the seal.
3. Box the bird.
4. Make an **h** under the tail of the fish.
5. Make an **i** over a box.

1. How many pigs did Pam have? _____

2. What was the name of the very small pig? _____

3. Did Pam have pig feed? _____

4. She planned to feed the pigs _____.
   • pig feed   • dog chow   • hot peppers

5. Were peppers ev<u>er</u> in the pan? _____

the front of a car •

driving a car •

loading a trailer •

planting seeds •

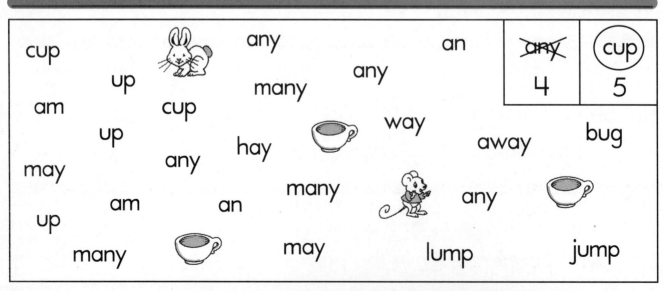

28

Pig
Pam
Six
Burp

1. Make a **U** in front of the bird.

2. Make a **5** in back of the car.

3. Circle the barn.

4. Box the bird.

1. How many pigs turned red? _____

2. Where did the red pigs go first?

   _____

   - to the drinking pan   - to the barn
              - to the field

3. Which pig did not turn red? _____

4. Which pig ate a lot of peppers? _____

5. Did Pig Six like those peppers? _____

6. What does Pig Six do to say thank you?

   _____

       - eats dirt   - burps   - yells

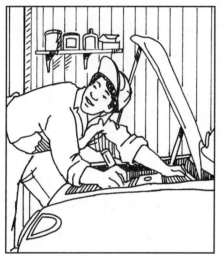

- "I can't drive you to town."

- "You can pick me up later."

- "I'll drive the tractor to the store."

- "Why is he late?"

- "I can run faster than this."

1. Make a **J** over the trailer.

2. Make a **D** over the tractor.

3. Box the car.

4. Circle the **J.**

_____

1. Jill lived _____ miles from town.

_____

2. What was her dad fixing? _____
      • a trailer   • a car   • a tractor

_____

3. How did Jill get to the store? _____
      • She ran.   • She swam.   • She hiked.

_____

4. Did she have to wait for her dad? _____

_____

5. What was he driving? _____
      • a cart   • a truck   • a tractor

p<u>oo</u>l	drink	steer
	ball	

TEST 3

30

1. _____   2. _____

3. _____   4. _____

Pam had red hot peppers. She had piles of peppers.
She said, "I think I'll feed these peppers to my pigs.
Those pigs eat everything."

So she loaded some peppers in a pot and a pan.

1. m<u>oo</u>n
2. smell
3. bang
4. sp<u>a</u>rk

1. ret<u>ur</u>n
2. almost
3. throwing
4. moment

1. front
2. every
3. bother
4. the<u>ir</u>

So Jill hiked to the store. When she got there, she got a cart and filled it. Then she waited for her dad in front of the store. He didn't show up. She began to think of things that may have made her dad late.

Jill told her dad, "It is time to go to the store."

"Well," her dad said, "I need to fix the car. So I can't drive you there now." Jill said, "I have a plan. I can hike to the store. You can pick me up later."

fold first

At last she saw him. Was he driving the car? No. He was driving a tractor with a trailer.

Jill loaded her bags into the trailer, and her dad drove her home.

The end.

fold

30

Jill lived on a farm that was six miles from town.

fun   otter   Ann

1. Make a ba__ll__ under the fire.
2. Box the clam.
3. Make an **R** on the shell.
4. Make a pan over the flames.

1. Did Ann like to stay in the sand with the other clams?

   _ _ _ _ _ _

   _____

2. She wanted to swim with the _____.

   _ _ _ _ _ _ _ _ _ _

   _____

   • sharks • boats • otters

3. Who told Ann that otters do not swim with clams?

   _ _ _ _ _ _ _

   _____

   • her dad • Bob • her mom

4. Who did Ann save? _____

   _ _ _ _ _ _ _ _ _ _ _

   _____

   • a shark • a little otter • her mom

5. The otter returned and let Ann hang on to

   _ _ _ _ _ _ _ _ _ _ _

   _____.

   • her tail • her nose • her dad

6. Did Ann like that? _____

   _ _ _ _

   _____

32

1. Who swims like a seal? _____

2. Who swims very slowly? _____

3. Who can't swim at all? _____

4. Who said, "You must be home before it gets dark"?

   • Bob   • Beth   • Bob's dad

5. Who said, "We will be back by then"?

6. What were the pals going to drive? _____

   • a bus   • a van   • bikes

many •   • a mole's home

food •   • a lot of things

hole •   • a note with a stamp on it

mail •   • a mom

mother •   • something to eat

bell	food	fall	drink	tractor	winter

Side 2

33

_____

1. How many pals had fun at the beach? _____

2. Which pal dove and swam like a seal? _____

3. Which pal went knee deep in the waves? _____

4. Which pal swam like a cat? _____

5. Who did Beth yell to? _____

> Jim went in the rain. He wore a big hat. Jim's hat got wet. But Jim did not get wet.

1. Jim went in the _____.
   - read
   - rain
   - road

2. What got wet? _____
   - his coat
   - his nose
   - his hat

dirty	peppers	small	m<u>oo</u>n	t<u>oo</u>th

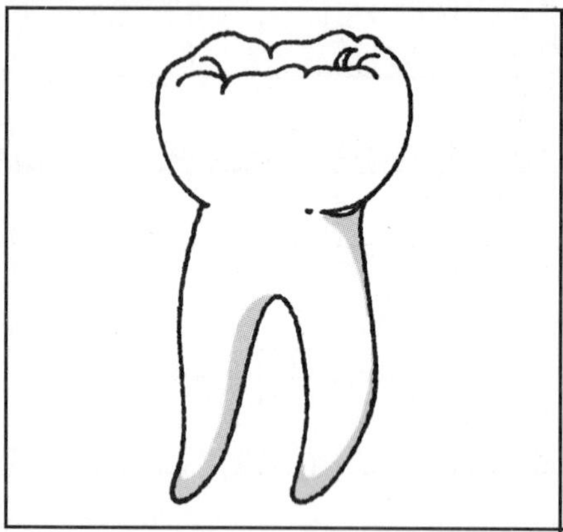

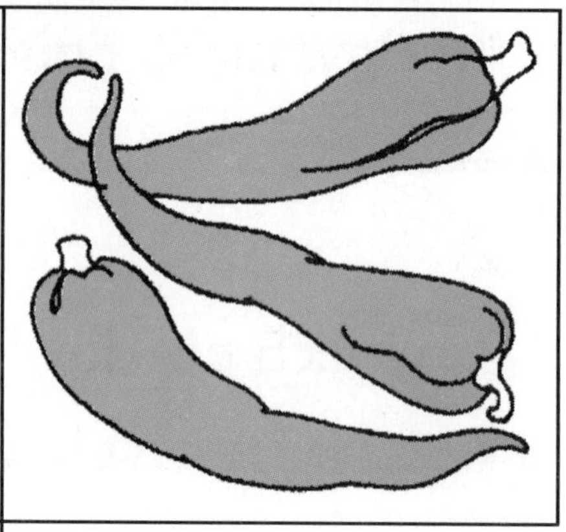

ten

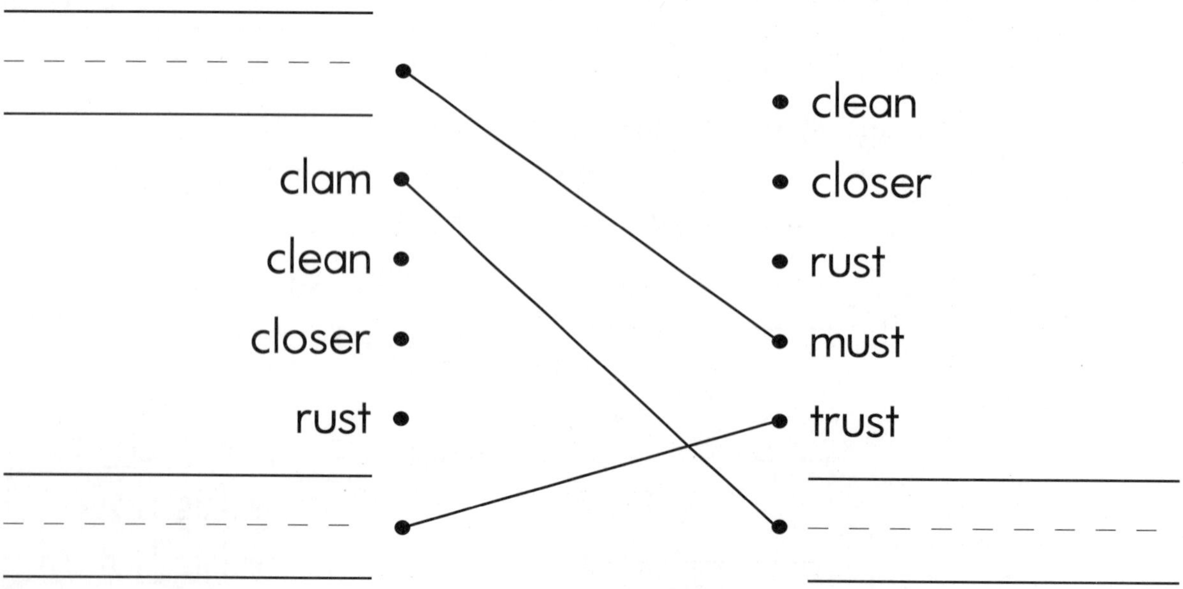

clam •
clean •
closer •
rust •

• clean
• closer
• rust
• must
• trust

_____

- - - - - - - - - - - - - - - - -

_____

34

1. Who tried to keep up with Bob? _____

2. Who got out of the waves and sat on the beach?

- - - - - - - - -

_____

3. Who called to Bob? _____

4. Who didn't hear Beth calling? _____

5. Who did Beth and Bob try to find? _____

1. Write an **S** over the bee.
2. Box the tail of the horse.
3. Write an **R** under the home.
4. Write a **W** on a wing.

She can hear barking. •

•

Snow is f<u>a</u>lling in a y<u>a</u>rd. •

•

He has a t<u>oo</u>l to fix the clock. •

•

The cow is sitting in the r<u>oa</u>d. The van can not drive by her. The man in the van is mad.

_____

1. Who is in the r<u>oa</u>d? _____

_____

2. Who is mad? _____

_____
— — — — — — — — — — — —
_____

1. Who was trying to find Tim? _____

_____

_____
— — — — — — — — — — — —

2. Where was Tim all that time? _____
    • in the van   • at home   • with Bob

_____

_____
— — — — — — — — — — — —

3. What was Tim doing? _____
    • running   • sleeping   • thinking

_____

_____
— — — —

4. Did the pals get home on time? _____

_____

_____
— — — —

5. Was Bob's dad happy? _____

_____

    1. Circle the thing you sit in.
    2. Make a **C** in the last tr<u>a</u>in car.
    3. Box the first tr<u>a</u>in car.
    4. Make a **V** at the end of the tr<u>a</u>in.

Side 1

A pig is on the tracks. The tr<u>ai</u>n has to stop. Six men lift the pig.

1. What has to stop? _____

2. How many men lift the pig? _____

baby   box   boat   farmer   raining   b<u>all</u>

The steer ran into the side of the tractor. There was a big bang. And something went flying. Was it the farmer or the tractor? No. The steer went flying. That steer landed on its back and said, "I hear bells ringing, and I see stars."

The end.

fold

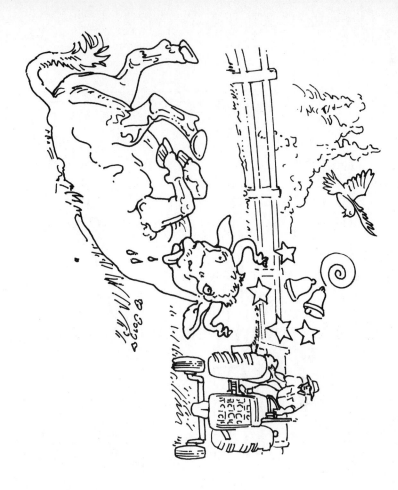

The Farmer and the Steer

35

There was a steer who lived on part of a farm. One day, the farmer drove his tractor to that part of the farm. The steer was sleeping in the field, and the farmer did not see the steer.

"I will dig rows," the farmer said. "Then I can plant corn in this field."

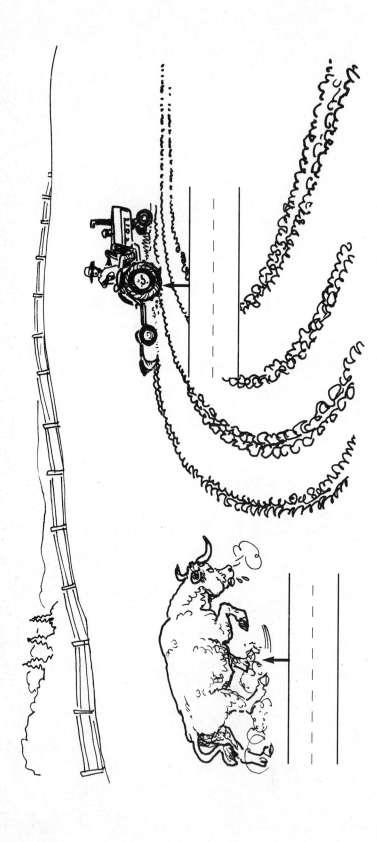

The tractor dug up one row, two rows, and three rows. When the tractor started to dig the next row, the steer woke up.

The steer said, "What is going on? I see a farmer and a tractor in my field. I don't like tractors or farmers here."

The steer got up and said, "I will send that farmer back to his home."

The steer went all the way to one side of the field. Then the steer ran at the tractor just as fast as a steer can run. The steer was thinking, "I will hit that tractor so hard that it will fall over. That farmer will go flying. Then he will leave."

•   • Don't swim in the deep part.

•   • Stay on the path.

•   • Don't let anyone in.

•   • You listen very well.

A fox made a cake that smelled like feet. Did anyone want a taste of the cake? No.

At last a rat tasted the cake. She liked it so much she ate it all.

1. What did the fox's cake smell like? _____

2. Who liked the fox's cake? _____

1

1. Tam started to play with _____.
   - snow balls
   - stones
   - the path

2. Who said, "I am here to fix the TV"?
   _____
   - Tom
   - Tam's mom
   - the robber

3. Who tried to sneak into a home?
   _____
   - the robber
   - Tam
   - a cop

4. Who called the cops? _____

5. Who told Tam that she was very smart?
   _____
   - a cop
   - Tam's dad
   - the robber

1. Circle the sail boat.

2. Put an **X** on the sail.

3. Make a box in front of the boat.

 •

• I can eat more than anybody else.

 •

• I can swim faster than anyone else.

 •

• I can read faster than anybody else.

 •

• I can throw better than anyone else.

Dan did not know how to ride a bike. He said, "I will try." Soon he was able to ride a bike.

Dan did not know how to fly. He said, "I will try to fly." Now Dan can fly a plane.

1. Dan did not know how to _____.

    • fly and ride   • eat and sleep   • run and jump

2. Dan was able to do things because he _____.

    • cried   • tried   • ate

3. What can Dan fly? _____

1. Where did the pack of rats live?

_____

– – – – – – – – – – – – – – – – – –

_____

- in a town   - in a hole   - on a farm

_____

2. How many rats kept yelling and bragging? _____

– – – – – – –

_____

3. Did the other rats like to listen to the bragging rats?

_____

– – – – – –

_____

4. One rat said, "I swim so fast I don't get

_____ "

– – – – – – – –

_____.

- a cake   - wet   - sad

_____

– – – – – – – – – – – – – – – –

5. What did the rats slip into? _____

- a hole   - a cave   - a pond

_____

– – – – –

6. Were the bragging rats good swimmers? _____

Side 2

38

moose	goose

1. The title of this story is "A Home in the _____.

    • F<u>or</u>est   • Zoo   • Farm

2. Who is the pal of the m<u>oo</u>se? _____

3. Where did they live? _____

    • in the field   • in the f<u>or</u>est   • in Bob's y<u>a</u>rd

4. Who had the plan to do something else? _____

5. The m<u>oo</u>se and goose want to live in a _____.

w<u>a</u>ll	peppers	y<u>a</u>rd
			broom

Jan liked to swim. She jumped into a lake. She swam with a duck. When she got out of the lake, she said, "I am all wet. I will sit in the sun to dry myself." So she did.

1. Who jumped into the lake? _____

2. Who swam with Jan? _____

3. How did Jan dry herself?

_____

1. Make a box under the broom.
2. Make a **C** on top of the tree.
3. Circle the snake.
4. Make an **X** next to the broom.

_____

- - - - - - - - - - - - -

_____

1. Which pal is able to fly to the zoo?

   - - - - - - - - - - - -

   _____

2. When did the goose see something in the pond?

   - - - - - - - - - -

   _____

   - morning   - sunset   - n<u>oo</u>n

   _____

   - - - - - - - - - - - - -

3. What was on a leaf? _____

   - two birds   - two bugs   - two fish

4. Who said, "We will fl<u>oa</u>t there"?

   - - - - - - - - - - - - -

   _____

		tree	story	~~tree~~	(star)
start	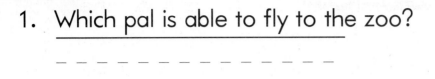	stars	3	5	6
steer	trees				three
stay	start	star	trees	star	
stay	tree	teeth		three	☽
tree		three	9	star	3

1. Make a box under the deer.

2. Circle the ram.

   _____

   - - - - - - - - - - - -

3. What is in front of the car? _____

4. Make a **w** under the car window.

   _____

   - - - - - - - - - - - -

5. What is in back of the car? _____

Jan went in a sail boat. The wind was blowing hard. So her boat went fast. When she was way out on the lake, the wind stopped. S<u>oo</u>n her boat stopped too. She said, "Oh well. I'll read." And she did.

Later the wind started to blow hard, and she sailed back to shore.

   _____

   - - - - - - - - - - - -

1. What did Jan go in? _____

   _____

   - - - - - - - -

2. Did the boat go fast? _____

   _____

   - - - - - - - - - - - -

3. What did Jan do after her boat stopped? _____

   • sleep   • read   • sit in the sun

Side 2

1. _____   2. _____

3. _____   4. _____

A pack of rats lived on a farm. Two rats in the pack made the other rats mad. These rats did a lot of bragging and yelling. They also told a lot of lies. The other rats called them the bragging rats.

1. yard	1. out	1. saying
2. tried	2. anyone	2. listen
3. small	3. want	3. follow
4. zoo	4. driving	4. happen

A pack of rats lived on a farm. Their home was not far from the pond.

There were two rats in the pack who made the other rats mad. These two rats did a lot of bragging and a lot of yelling at each other. They did not agree on which rat was the best at throwing, or which rat was the fastest at eating.

These rats told a lot of lies. The other rats called them bragging rats.

One time, the bragging rats did not agree who was the fastest swimmer. One rat said, "I can swim so fast that I pass up seals and otters."

The other rat said, "I can swim so fast I don't get wet."

As the two rats were bragging, it started to rain. The bragging rats slipped into the pond. They were not able to get out.

One rat said, "Help. This pond is too deep for me."

The other rats said, "We will help you get out, but you must stop saying how well you swim." The bragging rats agreed. After that, they never bragged about how well they swam, but they bragged about lots of other things.

The end.

41

_____

- - - - - - - - - - - - - - - -

_____

_____

- - - - - - - - - - - - - - - -

1. The pals planned to ride in a _____.

        • car   • balloon   • leaf

_____

        _____

        - - - - - - - - - - - - - - - - - - -

2. Which pal got cold feet? _____

_____

                _____

                - - - - - - - - - - - - - - - - - -

3. Which pal said that flying is fun? _____

_____

4. If the balloon falls from the sky, the goose will
    _____

    -
    _____.

        • fly away   • call Bob   • fall like a rock

_____

little •   • cake before it is baked

broom •   • something to sweep with

dirty •   • things that ring

bells •   • small

batter •   • not clean

1. Make a line under the f<u>o</u>rest.
2. Circle the cake.
3. Box the clock.
4. Make a big dot below the cake.

A man ate a big meal. Then he said, "I must brush my teeth." He was not able to find his t<u>oo</u>th brush, so he went to the store and got one. After he was done, he said, "My teeth shine like the m<u>oo</u>n."

1. Did the man eat a small meal? _____

2. What did he want to brush? _____

3. After he brushed, his teeth shined like the _____

   _____.

42

1. Who said, "I won't go without you"?

    _ _ _ _ _ _ _ _ _ _ _ _ _ _ _ _ _ _ _
    _____

    • the zoo keeper   • the moose   • the goose

2. Who didn't want to go in the balloon?

    _ _ _ _ _ _ _ _ _ _ _ _ _ _ _ _ _ _ _
    _____

                                    _____
                                    _ _ _ _ _ _ _ _ _ _ _ _

3. The pals got in the balloon in the _____.

    • morning   • noon   • afternoon

                          _____
                          _ _ _ _ _ _ _ _ _ _ _ _

4. Who kept talking? _____

                                    _____
                                    _ _ _ _ _ _ _ _ _ _ _ _

5. Who kept shaking with fear? _____

    leap •   • It has two wheels.

    happy •   • They grow food.

    bike •   • jump

    farmers •   • not sad

1. Circle the clock.
2. Make a pile of dirt next to the br<u>oo</u>m.
3. Make a **4** next to the barn.
4. Make an **X** over the clock.

Bob went to play in a park. His dad told him to be home before dark and not to get wet. Bob did not go in the swimming p<u>oo</u>l at the park, but it started to rain. Bob got home just before dark. His dad said, "You got wet."

_____

1. Where did Bob go? _____

2. Did Bob go swimming? _____

3. What did Bob do that his dad told him not to do?

_____

_____

Side 2

43

1. Before the balloon landed, the wind made it go

   _ _ _ _ _ _ _ _ _

   _____.

   • n<u>or</u>th   • east   • west

2. Did the balloon land in the moose home? _____

3. Where did the balloon land?

   _

   _____

   • in the f<u>or</u>est   • in the bab<u>oo</u>n home

            • in a pond

4. Did the folks at the zoo like what they saw? _____

1. Make an **m** below the washer.
2. Make a **T** over the basket.
3. Box the washer, but not the **m.**
4. Circle the basket, but not the **T.**

A fox sat under a tree. That fox was waiting for a rat. The fox wanted to play with the rat. The rat was in her home. The rat said to herself, "That fox may want to eat me, so I will stay here." And she did.

1. Who was under the tree? _____

2. What did the fox want to do with the rat? _____

3. Where did the rat stay? _____

been   moon   bean   ~~been~~   (m<u>oo</u>n)
           🌙   3   6

soon   been   🔴   room   began

broom   bees   noon   began   🌙

                   before   room   moon

soon
      ✏️   moon
        moose   noon   🌙   moon

between   bee   noon   boom 🕐
                                        been   bean

wise   old   plan   bragging

I have a _____ .

1. Write your name inside the cup.
2. Circle the moon.
3. Make a star next to the moon.
4. Box the thing that you drink from.

1. For a week, the bragging rats bragged about how _____ _____.
   - well they could fly
   - much they could eat
   - smart they were

2. Many things the bragging rats said were _____.
   - smart
   - lies
   - sad

3. By the end of the week, how did the other rats in the pack _____ feel? _____
   - tired of the yelling
   - happy
   - really smart

4. The other rats in the pack went to see _____ _____.
   - the wise old rat
   - Gorman
   - the bragging rats

5. What did the wise old rat have as part of his plan? _____ _____.
   - a stick
   - rope
   - feathers

6. The pack wanted the bragging rats to stop _____ _____.
   - singing
   - yelling
   - walking

_____

- - - - - - - - - - - - - - - - -

_____

   •

• I am the smartest.

   •

• We can't stand that bragging.

• I can do it for a week.

   •

• I have a plan.

The seal tried to eat a tin can. A pig walked over and told him to eat weeds. The seal went to the hill and ate seeds and weeds. Now the seal won't eat tin cans at all.

_____

- - - - - - - - - - - - - - - -

1. Who tried to eat a tin can? _____

_____

- - - - - - - - - - - - - - -

2. Who came over? _____

3. What did the seal eat?

_____

- - - - - - - - - - - - - - - - - - -

_____

1. Who had a plan to make the bragging rats stop

talking? _____
- the farmer   • the wise old rat   • a cat

2. The two bragging rats were bragging about how

_____ they were.
- smart   • old   • fast

3. The wise old rat told the bragging rats how to find out

who was the _____.
- oldest   • smartest   • fastest

4. He said that a smart rat can keep a feather on the end

of his _____.
- foot   • hand   • nose

1. Make a little line over the ant.
2. Circle Gorman.
3. Make a bird below the steer.

But where was Tim? They looked for him. They did not know he was sleeping in the back seat.

They saw him when the sun was setting and the moon was in the sky. Beth said, "We are late."

Bob's dad met the pals as they drove up. Was Bob's dad happy? No. Bob had to stay home for

fold

45

One day Bob said to his pals, "Let's go for a swim at the beach. We will have fun in the waves."

At first, the pals didn't feel like going with him. But after a while, they said, "Okay."

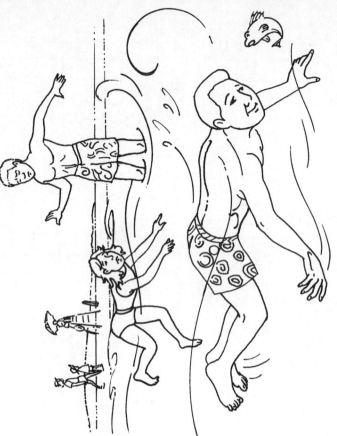

When the pals got to the beach, Bob dove into the waves and swam like a seal.

Tim went in the waves up to his knees and then said, "This is not for me."

Beth went in the waves for a while, but she didn't like it.

At last, Bob got out of the waves. "Wasn't that fun?" he asked Beth.

"No," she said. "Now let's get Tim and go home.

fold

Before Bob went swimming, he asked his dad.

Bob's dad said, "You can take the van. But you must be home before it gets dark."

"Yes," Bob said. "We will be back by then."

| it | better | do | longer |

I can do it _____
and _____ than you.

I know how to _____
do _____.

Beth made a pot of food. She said, "This food smells like it has too much pepper in it. I will let my brother taste it."

After her brother tasted the food, he yelled, "Hot, hot," and ran away.

1. Who made the food? _____

2. The food had too much _____.

3. What did her brother yell? _____

1. Who said that a smart rat can hold a feather on his

nose? _____

   • the wise old rat   • Gorman   • the bragging rat

2. Did the wise old rat set a feather on his nose? _____

3. What did the feather do when the wise old rat said

"you"? _____

   • stuck to his nose   • sailed into the air

       • turned green

4. <u>Is a rat able</u> to talk and keep a feather on his nose?

   _____

bells •   • bag

sack •   • jump

many •   • things that ring

leap •   • a lot of things

the   winner   smartest

I am _____ _____.

We don't have a
_____
_____.

---

snail   shark   balloon   cakes   lion

		clam

1. Was there a winner at the end of the first day?

   _ _ _ _ _ _

   _____

2. How many days did the bragging rats keep a feather on

   their nose? _____ _ _ _ _ _ _ _ _ _____

3. How did that make the other rats feel? _____

   _ _ _ _ _ _ _ _

   - sad   - happy   - sleepy

4. The bragging rats were happy because they felt

   _ _ _ _ _ _

   _____.

   - tired   - old   - smart

5. Every now and then, another rat told them _____

   _ _ _ _ _ _ _ _ _ _ _ _ _ _ _ _ _ _

   _____.

   - how smart they were   - what time it was

   - how to tell time

6. Which rat was really the smartest? _____

   _ _ _ _ _ _ _ _ _ _ _ _ _ _ _ _ _ _

   _____

   - the rat with yellow teeth   - the rat with the long tail

   - the wise old rat

48

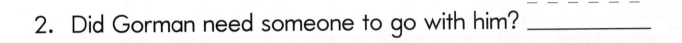

1. Who planned to go for a boat ride? _____
    - Bob   - Gorman   - a cow

2. Did Gorman need someone to go with him? _____

3. Who wanted to go with Gorman? _____

4. Who did Joan have to ask about boating?
    _____

    - her brother   - her mother   - a sister

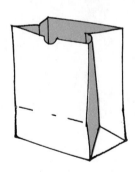

1. Circle the cup.
2. Write your name below the fox.
3. Make a **z** in front of the fox.
4. Box the sack.
5. Write an **r** on the sack.

A girl and her pal were on a sled. They went down a hill very fast. They ran into a pile of snow. The snow went flying everywhere. The girl said, "That was fun. Let's do it some more." So they did.

1. Who went down a hill on a sled?

_____

_____

_____

2. What did the sled run into? _____

3. The girl and her pal went down the hill some more _____

    _____

    because _____ .

shed	moose	bald	water	chop	fox

Gorman	toad	Joan

1. Who took Gorman to the water? _____

2. Who wanted to row the boat? _____

3. Who sat in the back seat? _____

4. Who said, "Get out of my home"? _____

5. Who said, "You can't stop us"? _____

1. Write an **M** below the queen.
2. Make a **T** next to the baby.
3. Circle the spoon.
4. Fix up the queen so she has black glasses.

Side 1

Two girls were playing in the snow. They got wet. Later, they got cold. Then they went home. When they got home, their mom made a fire and fixed some food. Now they are not cold or wet. The girls are happy.

1. What were the girls doing at first?

   _

   _____

2. How did they feel before they went home?

   _

   _____

3. When they got home, their mom made

   _ _ _ _ _ _ _ _ _ _ _ _ _ _ _ _ _ _

   _____.

   - snow and water   • rooms and a clock
            • a fire and food

Stars are over a tree. •   •

A shark is below an otter. •   •

A turtle is next to a plant. •   •

1. _____

2. _____

3. _____

4. _____

Just as the balloon was getting set to land on the r<u>oo</u>f of the moose home, a wind came up. The balloon went n<u>or</u>th. When the balloon landed, the moose l<u>oo</u>ked out and said, "We are not in the moose home."

---

1. somebody	1. ape	1. g<u>oo</u>d
2. everything	2. p<u>oo</u>r	2. long
3. wonderful	3. smartest	3. t<u>a</u>lking
4. below	4. f<u>ea</u>ther	4. w<u>a</u>nted

One time, the bragging rats yelled and bragged about how smart they were. The other rats were not able to stand it. They asked the wise old rat, "What can we do to stop the bragging rats from yelling?"

The wise old rat said, "I think I have a plan that will keep them from talking for many days."

The wise old rat said to the bragging rats, "There is a way to see who is the smartest.

A smart rat can stand so a feather stays on the end of his nose for a long time."

The rat with the long tail said, "I can do it way longer than that."

The wise old rat went on. "It is hard to keep the feather on your nose. If you talk at all, the feather will float away."

He set a feather on the end of his nose. Then he said, "You . . ." As soon as he talked, the feather went sailing into the air.

Both bragging rats said, "I know how to do it."

The wise old rat set a feather on the nose of each bragging rat. He said, "How long you keep the feather on your nose will show us how smart you are."

The bragging rats were still all day long. The wise old rat let them take time out to eat.

At the end of the day, they did not have a winner.

So they did the same thing for many more days.

Everybody in the rat pack was happy. The bragging rats were showing how smart they were. The rest of the pack did not have to listen to lies and yelling.

The end.

fold first

fold